This book is dedicated to the real Domingo,
who was disappeared by the Guatemalan army,
and to his family and all the other Maya who have
experienced—and who continue to experience—
so much social injustice and violence.

Text on page 91 credited to the Office of the United Nations High Commissioner for Refugees (UNHCR), "Introductory Note," *Convention and Protocol Relating to the Status of Refugees*, available from unhcr.org

Cover art Abraham Urias
Design by Tania Craan

Annick Press Ltd.

We acknowledge the support of the Canada Council for the Arts and the Ontario Arts Council, and the participation of the Government of Canada/la participation du gouvernement du Canada for our publishing activities.

Cataloging in Publication
Amado, Elisa, author
    Manuelito : a graphic novel / written by Elisa Amado; illustrated by Abraham Urias.

Issued in print and electronic formats.
ISBN 978-1-77321-266-1 (hardcover).--ISBN 978-1-77321-265-4 (softcover).
--ISBN 978-1-77321-268-5 (HTML).--ISBN 978-1-77321-267-8 (PDF)

1. Comics (Graphic works). I. Urias, Abraham, 1965-, illustrator II. Title.

PN6733.A485M36 2019   j741.5'971   C2018-905680-0   C2018-905681-9

Published in the U.S.A. by Annick Press (U.S.) Ltd.
Distributed in Canada by University of Toronto Press.
Distributed in the U.S.A. by Publishers Group West.

Printed in China

www.annickpress.com

Also available as an e-book. Please visit annickpress.com/ebooks for more details.

MANUELITO

A GRAPHIC NOVEL

WRITTEN BY **ELISA AMADO**

ILLUSTRATED BY **ABRAHAM URIAS**

annick press
toronto + berkeley

Sixty million people around the world become refugees every year. Half of them are under 18 years of age. They are fleeing their homelands because they fear that if they stay they will be killed. But this doesn't happen only in faraway places. It is happening in North America. Over 200,000 unaccompanied minors from the Northern Triangle of Central America—Guatemala, El Salvador, and Honduras—have made the very dangerous trip across Mexico, alone or with a coyote (a human trafficker hired by parents to take their children on this journey), in the hope of finding safety and refuge in the United States. Almost as many have been detained in Mexico at the request of the United States. Very few of these young people have access to outside lawyers or people who can help them. And many of them are now being hunted down by ICE—the United States Immigration and Customs Enforcement agency—and returned to the countries from which they fled, where their lives are in danger. Manuelito, a young Guatemalan boy and the hero of this story, is one of these people.

THIS STORY JUST HAPPENED TO ME EARLIER THIS YEAR. MY NAME IS MANUELITO. THIS IS MY FAMILY AND SOME OTHER PEOPLE FROM MY STORY. MY PARENTS PEDRO AND ROSA. MY GRANDPARENTS MANUEL AND CARMEN. THEY DIED A FEW YEARS AGO. MY MOTHER IS THEIR DAUGHTER.

MY MOTHER'S BROTHER TÍO DOMINGO. HE WAS DISAPPEARED WHEN HE WAS 12, ALMOST 35 YEARS AGO.

MY TÍA ADELA. SHE'S MY AUNT AND LIVED ON LONG ISLAND, USA.

BESIDES THE PEOPLE WHO LIVE IN OUR VILLAGE, THERE IS A CONVENT,
A SCHOOL, AND THE PACS—ARMED CIVIL PATROL. THEY ARE MEN FROM
THE VILLAGE. THE ARMY GAVE THEM WEAPONS. THEY ARE VERY DANGEROUS
BECAUSE THEY DON'T MIND KILLING PEOPLE THEY DON'T AGREE WITH.

A LONG TIME AGO, DURING THE WAR, THE ARMY GRABBED MY TÍO DOMINGO WHEN HE WAS PLAYING IN FRONT OF THE HOUSE. HE WAS ONLY 12. AFTERWARD, MY GRANDPARENTS AND ALL MY FAMILY, AND LOTS OF OTHER VILLAGERS, WENT AND HID IN THE MOUNTAINS FOR TWO YEARS. THEY ALMOST DIED OF HUNGER. DOMINGO NEVER CAME BACK. AFTER THE WAR, THEY DUG UP A HUGE GRAVE IN THE CONVENT'S GARDEN WHERE PEOPLE KILLED BY THE ARMY AND THE PACS HAD BEEN BURIED. BUT THEY DIDN'T FIND DOMINGO. HE HAD JUST DISAPPEARED.

MY GRANDFATHER MANUEL USED TO TALK ABOUT DOMINGO ALL THE TIME. THAT MADE MY GRANDMOTHER CRY. I DIDN'T LIKE ALWAYS HEARING ABOUT DOMINGO. BUT I WAS VERY SAD WHEN MY GRANDPARENTS DIED.

7

WE USED TO GO TO SCHOOL IN THE MORNINGS.
IT WAS BORING, BUT I'M GOOD AT MATH.

MY FRIENDS AND I PLAYED AROUND A LOT.

ROSITA LOVED HANGING AROUND WITH US.
SHE HATED TO BE LEFT BEHIND.

I want to go, too!

BUT SUDDENLY EVERYTHING BEGAN TO CHANGE. THE PACS WERE WALKING AROUND THE VILLAGE MORE AND MORE WITH THEIR GUNS. WE TRIED TO PRETEND THAT EVERYTHING WAS OKAY.

IT WAS TIME TO HARVEST
THE CORN AND WE HELPED.
BUT REALLY EARLY EVERY
MORNING, WE BEGAN TO SEE
LITTLE PLANES FLYING VERY
LOW OVER OUR HEADS.

ONE DAY, SOME GUYS WHO HAD TATTOOS ALL OVER APPEARED IN OUR VILLAGE. THEY WERE REALLY SCARY.

WHEN I WENT TO SCHOOL THE NEXT DAY, IT WAS CLOSED. NO ONE WAS THERE.

What am I going to do today?

Now that the narcos are around, the teachers are scared to stay here.
The government doesn't care about us. We have to do something.
You are too young to remember what happened last time when we tried to change things.
The kids are going to get in trouble.

NEXT, SOME OF THE OLDER KIDS FROM THE VILLAGE LEFT. WHEN THEY CAME BACK, THEY HAD TATTOOS ALL OVER THEM. THEY WERE IN GANGS NOW. MARAS. THEY STARTED ROBBING THINGS FROM PEOPLE. AND HITTING THEM.

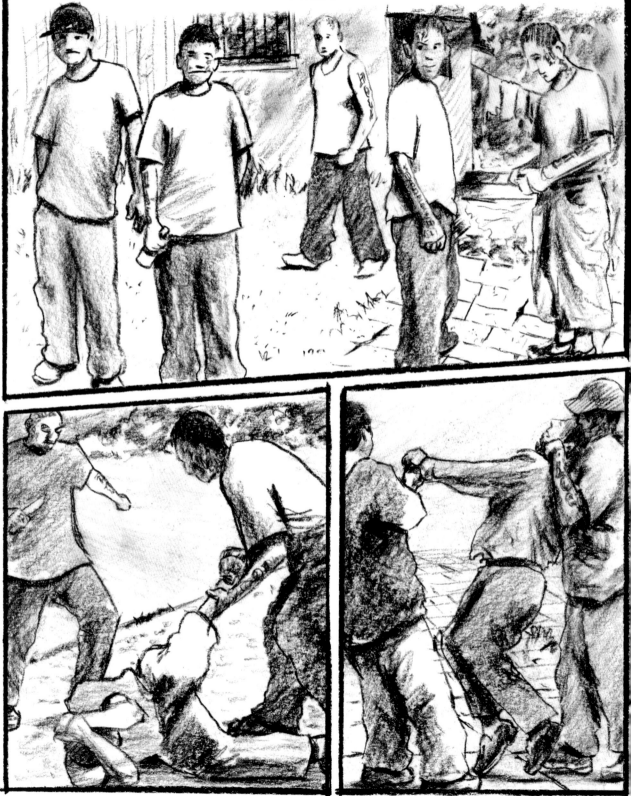

SOLDIERS KEPT COMING BACK. THEY STOPPED BUSES ON THE HIGHWAY. THEY PUSHED INTO OUR HOUSES.

THEY WERE GOING TO SEND ME TO THE USA. I THINK MY FATHER WENT TO THE BANK TO GET THE MONEY TO PAY SOMEONE THEY CALL A COYOTE TO TAKE US TO THE USA. I WAS SCARED. BUT I WAS EXCITED, TOO. THEY BOUGHT ME A CELL PHONE AND MY MOTHER SEWED A POCKET FOR MONEY INSIDE MY PANTS.

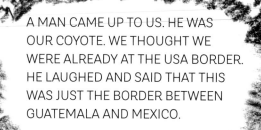

A MAN CAME UP TO US. HE WAS OUR COYOTE. WE THOUGHT WE WERE ALREADY AT THE USA BORDER. HE LAUGHED AND SAID THAT THIS WAS JUST THE BORDER BETWEEN GUATEMALA AND MEXICO.

HA HA HA!

Idiots. I'm in charge of you. Take off your clothes. Put your stuff in a plastic bag. Cross the river. I'll meet you on the other side.

What? All by ourselves?

I DON'T KNOW HOW WE MADE IT BECAUSE WE DIDN'T KNOW HOW TO SWIM, AND THE RIVER WAS REALLY STRONG. THE COYOTE TOLD US THAT THIS RIVER WAS MUCH EASIER TO CROSS THAN THE RIVER BETWEEN MEXICO AND THE USA. HOW MANY RIVERS WERE WE GOING TO HAVE TO CROSS?

THE BUS FINALLY STOPPED NEAR A SHELTER, A PLACE THAT YOU COULD STAY FOR A WHILE. THEY GAVE US A BED AND PROMISED SOME FOOD LATER. THE COYOTE DISAPPEARED AGAIN.

You kids got a really bad coyote. Everyone knows he's a bad man.

THE NEXT MORNING,
WHEN WE WENT
OUTSIDE, A POLICE
CAR DROVE BY.
WE RAN.

THE COYOTE SHOVED US INTO A CEMENT HUT AND SLAMMED THE DOOR. WE HEARD THE KEY TURN IN THE LOCK. COCO LOCO WAS CURSING AND SWEARING AND BEATING ON THE DOOR.

IT WAS REALLY HOT. FIRST IT WAS MORNING, THEN THE MIDDLE OF THE DAY, THEN IT STARTED TO GET DARK. MY PHONE WAS GONE. I WAS SO SAD.

Could I have saved Coco Loco?
What am I going to do?
I'm scared to go out.
I'm hungry.

WHEN I WOKE UP, I WAS STARVING. I LOOKED OUT AND HEARD VOICES. I SAW A GIRL WASHING HER FEET IN A LITTLE RIVER.

Hi, I'm Jenny. Who are you?

I'm Manuelito. Did you see a boy and a coyote?

JENNY TOOK ME TO A KIND OF CAMP WHERE THERE WERE WOMEN AND LITTLE CHILDREN. THEY GAVE ME SOME FOOD AND ASKED IF I WANTED TO CALL MY PARENTS.

I didn't go anywhere. Can I come home?
Better not. Let me talk to the Señora.
If you'll take Manuelito to the USA, his Tía Adela will send you money. Please take care of him.
Okay. We'll do our best. It's bad here, and the Coyote is really dangerous.

I WENT WITH THEM ON THE BUS. WE DROVE FOR TWO DAYS. I FELT SO MUCH SAFER.

Is the Señora your mother?

No, my parents sent me with them because the guy next door said he would rape me.

I'm from Honduras. I'm going to stay with my sister in Los Angeles. She works in a restaurant.

My parents were scared of the gangs.

FINALLY, WE GOT TO A RIVER THAT WAS ALMOST IN THE USA.

THE SEÑORAS TOLD ME THAT AFTER WE CROSSED THE RIVER, I HAD TO GO TO THE BORDER PATROL BY MYSELF AND TELL THEM I WAS SEEKING "ASYLUM" BECAUSE MY LIFE WAS IN DANGER.

WE CROSSED THE RÍO BRAVO TO THE USA.

THE NEXT DAY, THEY PUT SOME OF US IN A BUS AND TOOK US TO A PLACE THAT WAS LIKE A BIG HOUSE. PEOPLE GAVE US SOME CLOTHES AND SAID WE COULD STAY THERE UNTIL WE COULD GO TO OUR FAMILY IN THE USA.

63

THEY WERE NICE TO US THERE, BUT WE HAD TO TAKE CLASSES. THEY GAVE US SOME REALLY HARD BOOKS TO READ. BUT THEY WERE PATIENT. JENNY HELPED ME A LOT.

67

THE DIRECTOR CALLED US ALL TOGETHER. SHE SAID SHE WAS HEARTBROKEN, BUT THERE WAS NO MORE MONEY FROM THE NEW GOVERNMENT AND THE CENTER HAD TO CLOSE.

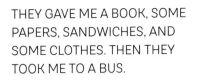

Don't talk to anyone. It will take about two days. Your aunt will be there. I'm sorry.

THEY GAVE ME A BOOK, SOME PAPERS, SANDWICHES, AND SOME CLOTHES. THEN THEY TOOK ME TO A BUS.

Again?

71

WE GOT ON ANOTHER BUS AND I FELL ASLEEP. THEN WE GOT OUT IN FRONT OF A TALL RED HOUSE. THERE WERE TREES ALL AROUND.
Come in, Manuelito. This is your new home. I live on the first floor. I'm glad you are here. You are safe now. Don't be scared.
Okay.

SHE SHOWED ME A SOFT SOFA WHERE I COULD SLEEP AND GAVE
ME SOME NEW CLOTHES AND PENCILS, PENS, AND PAPER.

Are the maras going to kill me now?
THEY TOOK US TO THE AIRPORT AND PUT US ON AN AIRPLANE. I'D NEVER BEEN ON ONE BEFORE, BUT I DIDN'T CARE. I SAW THE VOLCANOES OUT THE WINDOW. AND THEN WE LANDED.
Manuelito! Manuelito!

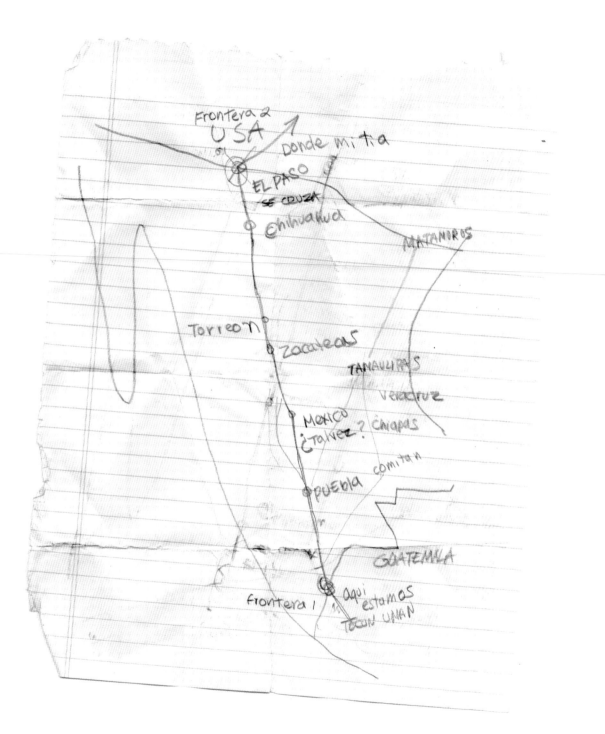

CENTRAL AMERICA

Manuelito's story begins in Guatemala, which together with El Salvador and Honduras is called the Northern Triangle of Central America. They are three of the most dangerous peacetime countries in the world. Ever since the 1950s, they have been a kind of battleground between forces inside and outside of their countries whose agendas have very little to do with taking good care of their citizens.

Over 400,000 people have died during this period. Many others have fled north to Mexico and the USA to seek safety and a place to live in peace.

In the second half of the twentieth century, the war was driven in part by the Cold War between the United States and the Soviet Union. But it was also about who would control the land—the natural resources and cash crops like bananas, sugar, and coffee—versus the desire of many of the citizens for social justice. A large percentage of the population is Indigenous, primarily Maya and Nahua, and descended from great, ancient civilizations.

According to a study by the United Nations Truth Commission (known as la Comisión para el Esclarecimiento Histórico in Spanish) undertaken after the war, 85 percent of the killings in Guatemala were committed by the army or by paramilitary groups, known as PACs (Patrullas de Autodefensa Civil). Though that war ended in the 1990s, the PACs are still a very strong presence in the Mayan villages.

Today, there is a new war that revolves around the drug trade. Huge drug cartels, known as *narcos*, the United States Drug Enforcement Administration (DEA), and local armies and gangs are fighting each other over the sale and distribution of illegal drugs. Central American countries do not produce drugs, but they are locations through which the cartels distribute and ship drugs, especially cocaine, to markets in North America and Europe. This is particularly true for Guatemala and Honduras. Local governments, armies, and police have been corrupted by the *narcos* and pressured by the DEA. There is a huge market for cocaine in the rest of the world, and people in rich countries are willing to pay a lot of money to gain access to it. The amount of money involved has led to the presence of many illegal forces inside the Central American countries, including gangs. After all, the money that comes from the sale of drugs is far more than most people can ever hope to earn. And it is now known that the war on drugs has not reduced the availability of drugs in their primary markets, North America and Europe.

Most people who live in the Northern Triangle want peace. They want to be safe, to be paid fairly for their work and the crops they produce, to be able to feed and educate their children, and to control what happens on their land. Tragically, these very basic human rights have been continuously denied them.

Withdrawing protection and deporting people from these countries who have sought refuge in the USA and Mexico is tantamount to condemning them to death. Yet the United States government, both under former president Barack Obama and, even more so today, under President Donald Trump, is sending large numbers of people, including those under 18, back to these countries. There are no jobs there for most of them. There is terrible violence, local governments are unable to protect their own citizens, and young people are the most vulnerable of all. This violates the UN Refugee Convention signed by all the governments involved.

Patricia Aldana

THE UNITED NATIONS CONVENTION AND PROTOCOL RELATING TO THE STATUS OF REFUGEES

The United States, Mexico, and Canada have all signed the Convention and Protocol Relating to the Status of Refugees. The Introductory Note by the Office of the United Nations High Commissioner for Refugees (UNHCR) in the official document includes the following statements:

- A refugee, according to the Convention, is someone who is unable or unwilling to return to their country of origin owing to a well-founded fear of being persecuted for reasons of race, religion, nationality, membership of a particular social group, or political opinion.
- Convention provisions are to be applied without discrimination as to race, religion, or country of origin.
- The Convention further stipulates that, subject to specific exceptions, refugees should not be penalized for their illegal entry or stay. This recognizes that the seeking of asylum can require refugees to breach immigration rules. It provides that no one shall expel or return a refugee against his or her will, in any manner whatsoever, to a territory where he or she fears threats to life or freedom.

ABOUT THE CREATORS

Elisa Amado is a Guatemalan living in Canada. She retains strong ties with her country of origin and has known many people whose lives have been disrupted, if not destroyed, by the conflicts that have occurred there since the 1950s. She has written a number of books, including *My Friend*, illustrated by Alfonso Ruano; *Tricycle*, illustrated by Alfonso Ruano (translated into Brazilian, French, and Korean); and *What Are You Doing?* and *Why Are You Doing That?*, both illustrated by Manuel Monroy. She is also the translator of many highly regarded books, such as *Two White Rabbits*, *Jimmy the Greatest!*, *Walk with Me*, and *On the Other Side of the Garden* by Jairo Buitrago and Rafael Yockteng; *Somos como las nubes/ We Are Like the Clouds* by Jorge Argueta; and the Napí series by Antonio Ramírez and Domi.

Abraham Urias was born in El Salvador, and as a little boy, he always liked drawing with chalk on his grandmother's living-room tile floor. When he was around 5 years old, while watching *Looney Tunes* and *The Flintstones*, he told himself that one day he would work for the studios that created his favorite cartoons. He loved growing up in El Salvador, but because of the civil war in his country, on May 8, 1981, at the age of 16, he immigrated to the United States. Since 1997, he has worked for one of the major studios in Hollywood doing what he always loved as a little boy. He created a character named Pelito and a book based on his childhood growing up in El Salvador. In 2014, along with 18 others, he created a project called Pelito Parks to build a playground in an impoverished area in Santa Ana, El Salvador, for kids who never had the chance to slide down a slide or hang from a monkey bar. He also gave away copies of his book to the children. His main objective was to bring fun and play to the kids of El Salvador who so often have to go to work at very young ages or leave their country to find a better life in the United States.

Patricia Aldana has had a long-standing interest in the lives of children in crisis. As Chair of the IBBY (International Board on Books for Young People) Foundation, she has studied and visited projects for refugee children around the world. She has been actively involved in the IBBY/REFORMA project for unaccompanied minors—children who have traveled alone from the Northern Triangle of Central America to seek asylum in the United States.